Struik Pocket Guides
for Southern Africa

Sharks
and
Stingrays

Rudy van der Elst

ILLUSTRATED BY
Roy Vermeulen

C. STRUIK PUBLISHERS

Rudy van der Elst, Senior Research Officer at the Oceanographic Research Institute in Durban, is the author of the best-selling *A Guide to the Common Sea Fishes of Southern Africa*.
Roy Vermeulen, who also lives in Durban, is a commercial artist.

Acknowledgements
I am indebted to several anglers and colleagues, in particular François Stemmet, Lorna Cameron, and Charmaine Branford.

Rudy van der Elst
Durban, 1986

Contents

C. Struik (Pty) Ltd
Struik House
Oswald Pirow Street
Foreshore, Cape Town 8001

Reg. No. 80/02842/07

First published 1986

Copyright © text and maps: R. van der Elst
Copyright © illustrations: R. Vermeulen
Copyright © illustrations pp.50-51: N. Kistnasamy

Cover design by Abdul Amien

Set by McManus Bros (Pty) Ltd, Cape Town
Reproduction by Hirt & Carter Ltd, Cape Town
Printing and binding by National Book Printers, Goodwood

ISBN 0 86977 290 2

How to use this book

This pocket guide is intended as a handy companion for those with an interest in the sea, be they naturalists or fishermen. Not only does it help with the identification of most cartilaginous fishes in our waters, it also provides a wealth of information about the life history and behaviour of these species.

Pages 50 and 51 cover the basic anatomy of the fishes dealt with in the book, in order to familiarize the reader with some of the structures that are described in the individual species entries. In that section, grouped by family, are detailed descriptions of chimaeras, sharks, skates, rays, sawfishes and guitarfishes (locally known as sandsharks). These families are arranged in an assumed evolutionary sequence, although in some cases fish of similar appearance have been grouped for benefit of the reader. Family names, the 'official' common name and any alternatives are given. However, it is the scientific name, consisting of two words, the first being the genus name and the second the species name, that is most definitive. The Afrikaans name is given at the end of the species entry.

Both the maximum and commonly caught average sizes are given, normally expressed as body length from tip of snout to tip of tail, but measured across the body width in the case of skates and rays. In those instances where there is uncertainty about a species' maximum size, this is indicated by means of a question mark after the maximum size.

Tooth counts can be diagnostic and it is for this reason that some appear in this book. The formula should be read as follows in this example:

$$\frac{12 - 1 - 12}{10 \text{ or } 11 - 2 - 10 \text{ or } 11}$$

meaning 25 teeth in the upper jaw of which one is central, flanked by 12 on either side. The lower jaw, therefore, has two central teeth with 10 or 11 on either side. The actual tooth shape may also be important, and some are given on page 53 as further aid to identification.

An indication of a species' local range can be obtained from the map provided.

The species accounts are devoted to interesting facts about sharks and their relatives, the way they live, their general behaviour and their value – or threat – to man.

Legends:
♂ = male
♀ = female

Species notes and illustrations

Elephantfish (Joseph)
Callorhinchus capensis
av. 50 cm; max. 100 cm

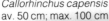

This curious and unmistakable fish is one of only four similar species that exist worldwide. Its probable common ancestry with sharks dates back nearly 300 million years, when sharks and elephantfishes were more numerous than they are today. Although the scaleless silvery body, single gill opening and lateral line seem un-shark-like, the anatomy and cartilaginous skeleton of the elephantfish confirm its close relationship to modern-day sharks. The mature male has long claspers and a stalked tactile appendage on the forehead, while the gut is also typically shark-like. The snout resembles a trunk and gives rise to its name. This common species lives on the bottom to depths of 200 m where it feeds on shellfish, molluscs and brittlestars which are crushed by the plate-like teeth. Internal fertilization precedes the production of two pointed egg cases during summer. This palatable fish is trawled and gill-netted in sizeable quantities. □ **Josef.**

CHIMAERAS (CHIMAERIDAE)

Chimaera (Rattail, Ghost shark)
Chimaera monstrosa
av. 90 cm; max. 150 cm

A close relative of the elephantfish, the chimaera is equally distinctive although it has a longer, tapering tail and lacks the snout projection. This primitive cousin of the sharks belongs to a family of some 35 species worldwide and may be found in most temperate seas. It leads a solitary existence in cooler deep waters and has been caught at a depth of 1 200 m. The fused, plate-like teeth are used to crush the food which consists of a variety of shellfish. The male can be distinguished by his claspers and the stalked projection on his forehead. The female is oviparous and each season lays two pointed egg cases on the seabed. Seldom, if ever, caught by anglers, the chimaera is common on some trawling grounds. Its flesh makes excellent eating. □ **Chimaera.**

COWSHARKS (HEXANCHIDAE)

Broadnose sevengill shark (Cowshark)
Notorynchus cepedianus
av. 120 cm; max. 290 cm

The combination of seven gill slits, single dorsal fin, flattened and broadly rounded head and numerous black spots on the body should readily identify this species. Primitive and very powerful, this shark enjoys a wide distribution throughout the world's temperate seas. It is common off the Cape coast, frequently being landed through the surf by anglers. Most of its time is spent close to the bottom where it feeds on other sharks, skates and rays, a variety of bony fish and even carrion such as mammal carcasses. Evidence from California implicates this species in attacks on humans. The ovoviviparous females produce up to 82 pups each season, usually born in very shallow water. The sevengill is a fine source of food, vitamin A-rich liver oil and high-quality leather, and as such represents a considerable resource worldwide. □ **Platneus-sewekiefhaai.**

Sixgill shark
Hexanchus griseus
av. 200 cm; max. 480 cm

An exceptionally large and heavy-bodied primitive shark instantly recognizable by its single dorsal fin set far back and its six gill slits. Its range includes all tropical and temperate seas. Adults mostly frequent outer slopes of the continental shelf to depths of almost 2 000 m, while juveniles may occur in shallower water and are occasionally trawled or caught by line. As it

lives both on the bottom and in midwater, its diet is varied and includes numerous species of fish, sharks, rays, squid, crabs, prawns and occasionally seals. Though common, not much is known about its life history, other than that it produces large litters of up to 100 pups. This is not a dangerous species despite its formidable six rows of comb-like teeth. In several regions this shark is a source of fresh fish, fishmeal and liver oil. □ **Seskiefhaai.**

DOGFISH SHARKS (SQUALIDAE)

Smallfin gulper
Centrophorus scalpratus
av. 80 cm; max. 100 cm

Although typically a dogfish shark with its cylindrical body, dorsal spines and absence of anal fin, the smallfin gulper may be distinguished by its small second dorsal fin. It is a deepwater species confined to the outer continental slopes and ranges in depth from 250-820 m. Consequently it is difficult to study its distribution, which may explain its reportedly patchy occurrence throughout the Indo-Pacific. Distribution also appears to be segregated by size and sex. This shark is common off Natal and is an active predator of a wide range of bony fish, other small sharks, squid, octopuses and some invertebrates. Each season, the female produces two young measuring about 35 cm. Although frequently caught by Natal's prawn trawlers, only modest quantities of this palatable shark are marketed. □ **Kleinvin hondhaai.**

Blackbelly lanternshark
Etmopterus lucifer
av. 30 cm; max. 45 cm

Lanternsharks may be identified by the enlarged second dorsal fin and stout grooved spines, relatively short snout, large eyes and absence of anal fin.

This, the most abundant lanternshark in South African waters, has a conspicuously dark underside and sharp, thorn-like denticles that make the skin particularly rough. It occurs in most oceans, living on or near the bottom at depths of 820 m which has prevented detailed study of its breeding habits; however, it is known that the birth size may be less than 16 cm, and that males outnumber females. Despite its small size, this lanternshark actively preys on smaller fish and crustaceans and is often found among deepwater pink prawn catches off Natal. Several members of this family have small luminous organs, known as photophores, along their sides. Not of any immediate value to man. □ **Swartpens-lanternhaai.**

Spiny dogfish
Squalus acanthias
av. 60 cm; max. 80 cm

This species can be identified by its two dorsal fins with ungrooved spines, the absence of an anal fin, the white spots on its body, and the first spine originating behind the level of the pectoral fin. An exceedingly abundant shark, it occurs in most temperate seas and ranges from surface waters to depths of 900 m. Through intensive study, it is known that it produces litters of one to 20 pups, each measuring about 20 cm. The slow growth rate of the spiny dogfish indicates that it attains maturity after about ten years and has a maximum lifespan of about 30 years. Despite its small size, this shark voraciously attacks a wide variety of prey, mostly bony fishes and squid. International catch statistics reveal that it is the most heavily exploited shark, although landings in the Atlantic have declined sharply. Caught on line or by trawl, its flesh is marketed for human consumption, petfood, fishmeal and other uses. When handling this shark, take care to avoid laceration by the sharp spines. □ **Penhaai.**

Bluntnose spiny dogfish
Squalus megalops
av. 50 cm; max. 71 cm

This and the very closely related longnose spiny dogfish may be distinguished from the spiny dogfish by having the first dorsal spine located directly over the pectoral fin, and by the absence of white spots. A widespread, strongly gregarious species, it lives near the bottom on outer continental shelves to depths of 730 m. Dense shoals may occur in some trawling grounds and analysis of their stomachs reveals a diet of lanternfishes, eels, other fishes, prawns and squid. An average of three pups, each measuring 23 cm, is born during winter after a two-year gestation period. The females grow to be much larger than the males. Although considerable quantities of this dogfish are caught off the Natal coast and despite its excellent food value, few are marketed.
☐ Stompneus-penhaai.

ANGELSHARKS (SQUATINIDAE)

African angelshark
Squatina africana
av. 90 cm; max. 108 cm

Angelsharks have free pectoral fins, a feature that immediately distinguishes them from sandsharks or guitarfishes which have pectorals fully fused to the body. The near-terminal mouth, visible when viewed from underneath, is equally diagnostic. Although at least 12 species occur worldwide, the African angelshark with its distinctive white spots is the only one in our region. This unusual bottom-living shark ranges from the surf zone to depths of 500 m and shows a preference for muddy regions such as the offshore Tugela Bank. Its diet consists mostly of

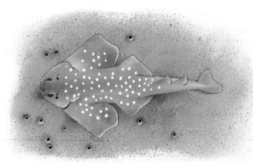

8

slow-swimming fishes, octopuses and squid. Development of the embryos is ovoviviparous and 7-11 young are born each season. The pups are about 30 cm long at birth and eventually attain maturity at 80-90 cm. Although an infrequent catch for anglers, trawlers do land solitary catches. Edible but seldom, if ever, marketed. □ **Afrikaanse engelhaai.**

BULLHEAD SHARKS (HETERODONTIDAE)

Bullhead shark (Horn shark, Port Jackson shark)
Heterodontus ramalheira
av. 60 cm; max. 83 cm

The combination of dorsal fin spines and presence of an anal fin distinguishes this shark. The only species of bullhead shark to occur in southern African waters, it frequents the warm waters of northern Natal, and generally ranges to depths of 275 m. Although not abundant, the bullhead is quite commonly reported from Natal's trawler catches. It is a slow-swimming shark that grovels in the sandy bottom for the crabs and sea urchins on

which it feeds. Similar species are known to take at least ten years to reach maturity, after which the oviparous females deposit about a dozen egg cases in specific nesting sites each season. It may take up to a year for the young to hatch. Bullhead sharks thrive in captivity, although further study is needed on this South African species. Edible but not utilized by man. □ **Bulkophaai.**

CARPET SHARKS (ORECTOLOBIDAE)

Zebra shark
Stegastoma fasciatum
av. 180 cm; max. 354 cm (?)

Although distinctive in colour and shape, the zebra shark may be further distinguished from other sharks (except the threshers) by having a tail equal to its body length. This sluggish, shallow-water species is found along most

tropical shores of the Indo-Pacific and is associated in particular with coral reefs. Divers on Zululand's reefs and on Aliwal Shoal have reported zebra sharks resting on the sandy bottom of gullies between reefs. They are thought to be nocturnal feeders, and their diet includes shellfish, mussels, crabs and small fishes. This unusual shark produces about four egg cases from which 20-36 cm-long young later emerge. The juveniles are unlike their parents, having brown bodies with striking yellow crossbars and blotches. Docile and completely harmless, the zebra shark is a source of food and sharkfin soup in the Orient. □ **Sebrahaai.**

Giant sleepy shark
Nebrius concolor
av. 250 cm; max. 320 cm

The arrangement of the fins and their angular shape are characteristic of this species. Primarily tropical with a widespread Indo-Pacific distribution, the giant sleepy shark ventures into Zululand waters during summer. Many divers have noted its inshore habits, especially around coral reefs where it may spend the daylight hours resting on the bottom. At night it forages for its food of miscellaneous reef organisms such as crabs, shrimps, sea urchins, octopuses, and small fishes, which are sucked up by a powerful muscular action of the pharynx. Although it is easily approached underwater, it is best not molested as it can deliver a powerful bite when provoked. About eight young are born to the ovoviviparous females each season. In the East this shark represents a source of food, soupfins, leather and liver oil. □ **Reuse-vaakhaai.**

WHALE SHARKS (RHINCODONTIDAE)

Whale shark
Rhincodon typus
av. 8 m; max. 18 m

This is the largest fish on earth, and with its distinctive pattern and prominent body ridges, cannot be confused with any other. Although distributed worldwide, it shows a preference for warm tropical waters, such as those off northern Natal. It is most common near the surface, ranging from the immediate surf zone to mid-ocean. Whale sharks often congregate in shoals of up to a dozen individuals. The enormous terminal mouth and sieve-like gill rakers are perfectly suited to its filter-feeding habits, which involve sucking in a variety of planktonic organisms such as krill, shrimps, anchovies, squid and even small tuna-like fishes. Floating organisms (nekton) are also consumed when the whale shark cuts through the surface. This huge but harmless animal is often accompanied by gamefish such as cobia and is easily approached underwater. There is some uncertainty about its mode of reproduction, but it is thought to be oviparous with the seasonal birth of some 16 pups, each about 55 cm long. □ **Walvishaai.**

BASKING SHARKS (CETORHINIDAE)

Basking shark
Cetorhinus maximus
av. 8 m; max. + 10 m (?)

Second only to the whale shark in size, this species may be distinguished by its enormous gill slits, absence of body ridges and by the notch in its upper caudal fin. The basking shark prefers the cooler coastal waters of the world and appears to be more common in the northern hemisphere. Endowed with

a massive structure of gill rakers (that are replaced annually), it is capable of straining tons of plankton from surface and deeper oceanic waters. Although mostly solitary, seasonal shoaling occurs for courtship and feeding, during which time they are vulnerable to being harpooned. This highly migratory shark is thought to be ovoviviparous with uterine cannibalism, as is the case with ragged-tooth sharks. They are most often seen basking in surface waters or washed up dead on beaches. Several fisheries exploit this shark for its edible flesh, soupfins, oil, squalene and leather. □ **Koesterhaai.**

RAGGED-TOOTH SHARKS (ODONTASPIDIDAE)

Spotted ragged-tooth (Grey nurse shark,
Sand tiger) *Eugomphodus taurus*
av. 280 cm; max. 320 cm

With its large, robust body, conical snout, small eyes and long mouth armed with rows of slender pointed teeth, the ragged-tooth is unmistakable. Harmless despite its formidable appearance, this is a common inhabitant of coral and rocky reefs in most warmer seas of the world. Its preference for shallow water, its sluggish swimming habits and, frequently, attendant remoras, make it a popular spectacle for scuba enthusiasts. The ragged-tooth feeds on slower-swimming fishes, stingrays and other small sharks by first approaching them stealthily and then lunging. It is one of the few larger sharks that can actively 'pump' water over its gills in order to continue breathing while remaining motionless. This also requires buoyancy control which it achieves by periodically swallowing air from the surface, thereby enabling it to hold its heavy body at a desired depth. Although mostly solitary, ragged-tooth sharks congregate in shoals each summer at specific

mating sites, such as the St Lucia Marine Reserve. The females are fertilized internally and, when pregnant, move to the cooler eastern Cape waters to produce one or two pups, each measuring 100 cm. Their breeding involves uterine cannibalism: the dominant pup in each uterus devours its 16-23 siblings to obtain nourishment during the 6-9 months of pregnancy. The numbers of ragged-tooth sharks have been reduced locally as a result of their vulnerability to protective shark nets. The Japanese consider this shark good eating. □ **Spikkel-skeurtandhaai.**

The spotted ragged-tooth periodically comes to the surface to swallow air which it needs for buoyancy control.

MACKEREL SHARKS (LAMNIDAE)

Great white shark (Blue pointer, White death)
Carcharodon carcharias
av. 300 cm; max. +640 cm

This, the largest and most fearsome of all predatory sharks, occurs throughout the world's major oceans although it prefers cooler waters in proximity to land. Identification is based on its great size, very small second dorsal fin, large triangular teeth and pronounced lateral keels on the tail. The great white is frequently found preying on seals near their colonies or scavenging whale carcasses wherever whaling is still practised. Notorious for its many confirmed and fatal attacks on humans, the great white is also responsible for numerous unprovoked attacks on boats. Its bold and direct

attack is believed to be a successful feeding strategy to outwit the fast, more intelligent seals and dolphins on which it feeds. Despite its potential threat to bathers, this species occupies an important place in the ecosystem, especially in its natural control of seal populations.

Some speculation remains over the true maximum size that this shark can attain. While prehistoric relatives of this species measured 12 m, the largest great white reliably recorded is 6,4 m. However, recent (unconfirmed) reports suggest that larger specimens may still exist.

The great white is mostly solitary, although smaller specimens may form packs of up to ten. Remarkably, not a single pregnant female has ever been recorded and virtually nothing is known about this species' reproduction.

This shark is a very active swimmer and tagging experiments have confirmed its great cruising and endurance ability. While many are seen at the surface near the mainland, others have been caught at depths of 1 200 m, often near oceanic islands. □ **Witdoodshaai.**

See also front cover illustration and detail of great white's teeth on page 53

Seals are a favourite prey of the great white shark.

Shortfin mako
Isurus oxyrinchus
av. 180-250 cm; max. 400 cm

A typical mackerel shark with its spindle-shaped body, pointed snout, vicious teeth, lateral keels and small second dorsal and anal fins, the shortfin mako is best identified by its pectoral fins that are shorter than its head length. This widely distributed oceanic shark is one of the swiftest fishes known which, together with its spectacular jumping behaviour, makes it one of the most sought-after gamefish. However, it is also known to be dangerous and is particularly unpredictable when hooked or otherwise molested. This mako feeds actively on a large variety of tunas, bonitos, other gamefish and smaller fish prey, but surprisingly few marine mammals are ever attacked. Uterine cannibalism occurs in this ovoviviparous species and females produce 4-16 young, each measuring about 70 cm at birth. Makos make fine eating and the catches made by longlining are marketed mainly in the United States of America and in Japan. □ **Kortvin-mako.**

THRESHERS (ALOPIIDAE)

Thresher
Alopias vulpinus
av. 350 cm; max. 600 cm

With its tail fin equal in length to the body, and its noticeably small eyes, this powerful gamefish is most distinctive. A relatively common shark, it is widely distributed throughout the world's warm and temperate seas, with individuals ranging from the shallows to depths of 350 m. The thresher is

known for its ability to herd small shoaling fishes and squid before stunning them with a whip-like action of its tail and then actively devouring the injured prey. Not surprisingly, many threshers are hooked in the tail when caught by longliners or sport fishermen. Litters of two to six pups are born to the ovoviviparous females and there is evidence of uterine cannibalism. Despite its size and active behaviour, the thresher is not considered dangerous to man. Its flesh and other by-products are highly valued in several countries.
□ **Sambokhaai.**

Bigeye thresher
Alopias superciliosus
av. 350 cm; max. 460 cm

Although typically a thresher, the somewhat shorter tail, deep groove on the head and the noticeably larger eyes distinguish this shark from any other. Its circumtropical distribution exposes it to many fisheries around the world, especially deeper-set longlines. While this shark does occur in surface waters, it prefers abyssal regions of the ocean, to depths of at least 500 m. Its larger eyes probably facilitate feeding in these twilight zones, especially as its diet often consists of deepwater lanternfishes, hakes and similar species. The ovoviviparous females produce two to four pups each season, presumably after uterine cannibalism. Besides its edibility, this thresher is a source of vitamin A, oils, soupfins and leather. It is also a fine sport fish and is often caught together with swordfish, using chemical lights (Cyalume lures).
□ **Grootoog-sambokhaai.**

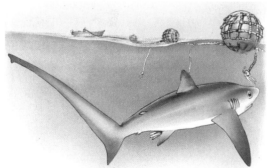

Puffadder shyshark
Haploblepharus edwardsii
av. 40 cm; max. 60 cm

Shysharks, which belong to the family of catsharks, may be distinguished by the greatly expanded nasal flap that reaches the mouth. The puffadder shyshark is most distinctive with its attractively variegated patterns and colours, although there are differences between Cape and Natal specimens. A common shallow-water endemic, it is frequently caught by Cape anglers but occasionally is also trawled off the Natal coast. Its diet, reflecting its sluggish existence, includes crabs, bottom-living fishes and squid. Each season, the oviparous female produces two egg cases from which 10 cm-long pups hatch. Although edible, the flesh is not utilized and is generally discarded. □ **Pofadder-skaamhaai.**

Brown shyshark
Haploblepharus fuscus
av. 50-60 cm; max. 73 cm

Similar to other shysharks in shape, this species lacks any distinctive patterns and is larger. It is common, especially in shallow sandy and rocky areas of the southern and eastern Cape. This bottom-living and sometimes cave-dwelling shark typically curls up when molested or captured, and covers its eyes with its tail, hence its name shyshark. The diet of this sluggish shark comprises crabs, crayfish and various smaller bottom-living fishes. The oviparous female probably produces two egg cases each season, but this has not yet been recorded. Although edible, this is not a popular catch. □ **Bruin skaamhaai.**

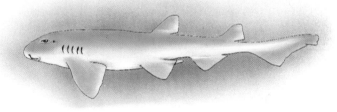

Dark shyshark

Haploblepharus pictus
av. 40 cm; max. 56 cm

The distinctive colours and variegated patterns distinguish this from other sharks. Like the puffadder shyshark, this species is endemic and occurs most commonly in shallow sandy areas around the Cape coast. Its diet consists of slow-swimming, bottom-dwelling animals such as crabs and small fishes, confirming its sluggish behaviour. Each season mature females lay two egg cases, each measuring about 6 cm. Although edible, this is not a popular catch. ☐ **Donker skaamhaai.**

Banded catshark

Halaelurus lineatus
av. 45 cm; max. 56 cm

This species is best identified by its characteristic colours and patterns which include about 26 dark, narrow vertical bars on a pale brown body. Its upturned snout and comparatively small dorsal fins are also distinctive. There are at least ten species in this genus of warm-water sharks, and three of them occur in southern African waters. The banded catshark is common in shallow water but appears equally abundant at depths ranging to 300 m. With a distinct preference for sandy bottoms, this species feeds mainly on prawns and crabs and, occasionally, small fish. It adapts well to captivity and aquarium observations have revealed that during winter the female produces a dozen or more well-advanced egg cases, from which juveniles hatch a month later. The hairy egg cases with their long tendrils are frequently found attached to the mesh of Natal's shark nets. Females predominate in catches, suggesting that sexual segregation may occur, possibly according to depth. Although caught by anglers and trawlers, it is usually returned to the water. ☐ **Band-kathaai.**

Tiger catshark
Halaelurus natalensis
av. 40 cm; max. 47 cm

Similar in appearance to the banded catshark, the tiger catshark differs by having about ten double bands across the body and by its somewhat larger dorsal fins. Although the original specimen was allegedly caught off Natal, this species appears to be confined to cooler Cape waters and rarely overlaps with the distribution of the banded catshark. It is an endemic and ranges from the shallows to depths of at least 125 m, from where it is netted by trawlers, especially in Algoa Bay. The diet of this shark consists of fish, crustaceans and occasionally squid, most of which are caught on or near the bottom. About 6-9 fairly tough egg cases with robust tendrils are produced by the oviparous females, and are already well developed when deposited on the ocean floor. Most catches of this species are discarded. □ **Tier-kathaai.**

Striped catshark
Poroderma africanum
av. 70 cm; max. 100 cm

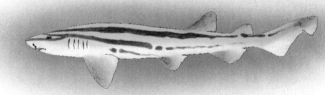

This large and robust catshark is endemic to South Africa and can instantly be identified by its pattern of distinct longitudinal lines. It has sluggish habits and spends most of the daylight hours resting on shallow rocky bottoms or hiding in caves. At dusk it becomes more active and during the night preys on small fish, crabs, crayfish and squid. The female produces only two young each season, and these hatch from 'mermaid's purse' egg cases that are attached to kelp or other submerged objects. Commonly netted by trawlers and caught by anglers at night, this edible species is not highly prized by fishermen. □ **Streep-kathaai.**

Blackspotted catshark
Poroderma marleyi
av. 50 cm; max. 65 cm

The combination of long nasal barbels and distinctive large dark spots arranged in longitudinal rows distinguishes this catshark from any other. It is a moderately abundant, shallow-water endemic with a preference for sandy and rocky bottoms. Its diet includes small crabs and other invertebrates. Young are produced from egg cases that the females attach to underwater objects and vegetation. It is frequently caught by anglers and sometimes trawled to a depth of 50 m. Edible but not prized. □ **Swartkol-kathaai.**

Leopard catshark
Poroderma pantherium
av. 60 cm; max. 84 cm

Strikingly leopard-like patterns immediately identify this endemic, although markings may vary in specimens from different localities. Nocturnal, it ranges from the shore to depths exceeding 250 m, and is regularly caught by both surf anglers and deep-water trawlers. Each female produces only one or two eggs per season in the form of 'mermaid's purses' attached to some underwater structure. Diet consists of small bony fishes, crustaceans and squid. Not normally utilized for food. □ **Luiperd-kathaai.**

REQUIEM SHARKS (CARCHARHINIDAE)

Soupfin shark (Tope, School shark)
Galeorhinus galeus
av. 120 cm; max. 180 cm

The soupfin shark may be distinguished from many other seemingly similar sharks by its longer snout, slender body and horizontally oval eyes. The

second dorsal fin is noticeably smaller than the first. This abundant shark is found in all temperate seas, especially along the western seaboard of continents. Although confined to continental shelves, the soupfin shark may reach depths of 450 m and is known to undertake lengthy seasonal migrations. Virtually all forms of marine animal life, especially shoaling fishes and squid, fall prey to its sharp teeth and powerful jaws. The ovoviviparous females each produce a litter of up to 52 pups in shallow nursery areas. Its shoaling behaviour facilitates commercial exploitation and many large fisheries have been based on this species to utilize its excellent meat, vitamin A-rich oil and especially its fins for sharkfin soup. Gansbaai's famous fish biltong is usually prepared from this shark which is also popular with many sport anglers. □ **Vaalhaai.**

Houndshark
Mustelus mosis
av. 70 cm; max. 150 cm

Although similar to many of the other 20 species that belong to this genus worldwide, this houndshark is the only one of its type found off Natal and Transkei. It is distinguished by its uniform colour and unmarked body, although some specimens have a white-tipped first dorsal and black-tipped second dorsal fin. A common shark, it inhabits inshore waters, usually over sandy bottoms, where it feeds on molluscs and shellfish that it crushes with its rows of molar-like teeth. The females are viviparous and each season produce 6-10 pups, many of which spend their early life in the surf zone. This solitary shark is often caught by shore and skiboat anglers and occasionally is trawled in deeper water. Despite its excellent flesh it is usually discarded. □ **Hondhaai.**

Flapnose houndshark (Quecket shark)
Scylliogaleus quecketti
av. 70 cm; max. 102 cm

Clearly a houndshark in appearance, the flapnose differs by having a shorter snout, a comparatively large second dorsal fin and very large nasal flaps that partly cover the mouth. This shark is endemic to east coast waters and is commonly found in the shallows, especially just beyond the surf zone. It is a fairly sluggish shark that preys mostly on crabs and crayfish, crushing them with its rows of molar-like teeth. Some 2-4 pups are born after an estimated nine-month gestation period. The flapnose houndshark is often landed by rock and surf anglers fishing from headlands along the lower Natal and Transkei coasts. It is edible. □ **Flapneus-hondhaai.**

Spotted gullyshark (Sweet William, Sharptooth houndshark) *Triakis megalopterus*
av. 120 cm; max. 174 cm

This robust shark may be distinguished from similar species in this region by its bluntly rounded snout, conspicuous black spots and the sharp, erect cusps that occur on its rows of pavement-like teeth. Curiously, the spots are not always present and as a result this shark is often confused with the smooth houndshark (*M. mustelus*) that occurs in the same region but which has rows of smooth teeth. This common endemic of shallow coastal waters is usually found over sand, especially in False Bay. Its habit of swimming very close to the bottom is thought to give it the element of surprise necessary to prey on other, smaller, bottom-living sharks, bony fishes and crabs. About ten pups are born to each ovoviviparous female, probably after they congregate in very shallow water during summer. Although they make good eating and are commercially exploited, most spotted gullysharks are released by anglers. ☐ **Gespikkelde sloothaai.**

Silvertip shark
Carcharhinus albimarginatus
av. 150 cm; max. 275 cm
Tooth formula $\dfrac{13-1 \text{ or } 2-13}{12-1 \text{ or } 2-12}$

The conspicuous white tips to the rear edges of all fins, presence of an interdorsal ridge and small second dorsal fin render this shark unmistakable. Widely distributed throughout the warmer Indo-Pacific, the silvertip is pelagic and seldom ventures close inshore but is particularly common around oceanic islands. Although often seen following ships at sea, this shark has been caught at depths exceeding 600 m, which demonstrates its wide dietary preference for both surface- and bottom-living fishes. Viviparous, the silvertip pups during summer, producing litters of up to 11 young, each measuring about 80 cm, which spend their adolescence in shallower waters. Despite the absence of documented attacks on humans, this very bold and aggressive shark should be considered potentially dangerous and treated with circumspection, especially when spearfishing. It is edible and mostly caught on longline. ☐ **Silwertiphaai.**

Oceanic whitetip shark
Carcharhinus longimanus
av. 200 cm; max. 350 cm
Tooth formula $\dfrac{14-2-14}{14-2-14}$

A most distinctive shark with its stocky body, lobe-like fins and mottled white tips to the first dorsal, the caudal and pectoral fins. Black tips mark the anal and pelvic fins. This is a truly oceanic shark which enjoys a wide distribution throughout the world's warmer oceans. Few ever approach land masses and most catches are recorded over deep water, some at a depth of 500 m. The oceanic whitetip is a solitary species but is often accompanied by pilotfishes as it cruises in search of food which consists of a variety of pelagic bony

fishes, squid, and occasionally turtles as well as marine mammal carrion. When Durban's whalers were still operating, this shark frequently attacked carcasses; it can be quite bold in its pursuit of prey and verified attacks on divers and shipwrecked swimmers highlight its potential threat. During summer, the viviparous females produce litters of 1-15 pups. Frequently caught on longline as a source of food, oil, leather and soupfins. □ **Opeseewittiphaai.**

Copper shark (Bronze whaler, Narrowtooth shark)

Carcharhinus brachyurus
av. 150 cm; max. 292 cm

Tooth formula $\dfrac{15-1-15}{15-1-15}$

This shark is easily mistaken for several others and requires careful examination before a positive identification can be made. The elongated snout, absence of distinctive markings on the fins and normally absent dorsal ridge are important features. Most characteristic are the upper teeth which have strongly bent cusps pointing sideways. Abundant and widely distributed, the copper shark occurs predominantly in slightly cooler coastal surface waters and also to depths of 100 m. Its diet includes a wide variety of surface and bottom-living fishes, smaller sharks, stingrays and squid. This shark is well known for its seasonal pursuit of sardine shoals as these migrate to Natal. The viviparous females produce litters of 13-20 pups, each measuring 60-70 cm at birth. This is a fine sport fish as many West Coast and Namibian anglers will attest. Good eating. □ **Koperhaai.**

Blacktip shark (Blackfin shark)

Carcharhinus limbatus
av. 150 cm; max. 255 cm

Tooth formula $\dfrac{15 - 2 \text{ or } 3 - 15}{15 - 1 - 15}$

This and several other requiem sharks are often collectively called blackfin.
C. limbatus is distinctive, however, and may be positively identified by its
pointed snout, absence of a dorsal ridge, its erect pointed teeth and black
tips to all fins except the anal. The conspicuous pale band along each flank
on the otherwise grey body also aids identification. This tropically distributed
shark is one of the fastest and most active inshore predators along our east
coast, frequently leaping out of the water in pursuit of its prey. The blacktip
feeds predominantly on bony fish and it is particularly abundant during the
May mullet run at St Lucia and the winter sardine run. Although
spearfishermen are often harassed by this bold shark, no authenticated
records of attack exist. There is a one-year gestation after which females
give birth to a maximum of ten pups. Blacktip sharks are fine sport fish and
make good eating. ☐ **Swarttiphaai.**

Dusky shark (Ridgeback grey shark)

Carcharhinus obscurus
av. 120 cm; max. 365 cm

Tooth formula $\dfrac{14 \text{ or } 15 - 2 - 14 \text{ or } 15}{14 - 1 - 14}$

The absence of any noticeable markings on the grey body and the obvious
interdorsal ridge are typical of this shark, although its distinction from other
sharks requires more careful study. However, its abundance in southern
African waters is so much greater than that of other species that the
probability of confusion is unlikely. The dusky is widely distributed in warm
and temperate seas and ranges from the surf zone to the outer edges of
continents, sometimes to depths of 400 m. Whereas the adults predominate
offshore, the young remain close to the shore, having been born there during
summer. Here they may be preyed on by larger sharks of other species

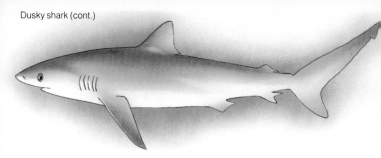

which, in turn, fall victim to shark nets. In recent years this has reduced predation causing juvenile duskies to proliferate and create a potential ecological imbalance. This species is a formidable predator of a wide variety of bony fishes and can be most troublesome when offshore trawlermen retrieve their nets. Packs often follow vessels at sea and certainly should be considered dangerous. Large catches of young duskies often constitute the bulk of catches at angling tournaments. The edibility of this species is generally underestimated. □ **Donkerhaai.**

Zambezi shark (Bullshark)

Carcharhinus leucas
av. 200 cm; max. 350 cm

Tooth formula of *C. leucas* $\dfrac{13-1-13}{12-1-12}$

Tooth formula of *C. amboinensis* $\dfrac{12-1-12}{11-1-11}$

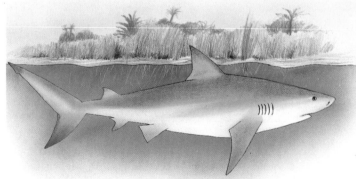

The widely distributed Zambezi can be distinguished from other requiem sharks by its more robust body, broadly rounded, very short snout and broad, triangular, serrated teeth in the upper jaw. However, it closely resembles the Java shark (*C. amboinensis*), and the two can only be distinguished by differences in their fins: the first dorsal is at least 3,2 times higher than the second in the Java, but less than this in the Zambezi. Both species are grey without any distinct markings, although the juveniles of both do have darkened tips to their fins. The two species are equally abundant in our coastal waters: the Zambezi prefers shallow estuarine waters, while the Java lives slightly deeper. During summer, pregnant female Zambezi sharks drop their 70 cm-long young close to estuaries, especially St Lucia, Richards Bay and Tugela, where they remain until adolescence. In contrast, Java shark pups are very rare along our coast. The Zambezi feeds predominantly on estuarine fishes, especially stingrays, small sharks, mullet and many other bony fishes. The remains of birds, land mammals, turtles and miscellaneous debris are also found in their stomachs, emphasizing the potential danger of this species to bathers. It has probably been the cause of several shark attacks in Natal, although the Java shark may also be implicated. Although shark nets have reduced its abundance, the Zambezi remains a powerful quarry for anglers. Both species are edible. ☐ Zambesihaai.

Spinner shark (Longnose grey shark)
Carcharhinus brevipinna
av. 150 cm; max. 280 cm
Tooth formula $\dfrac{16-2-16}{16-1-16}$

The elongate body with its smooth back, long pointed snout and small eyes are characteristics of the spinner shark, and those specimens exceeding one metre have darkened tips to the fins, including the anal fin. The upper jaw teeth are erect and have narrow pointed cusps. This widespread warm-water shark is common in coastal surface waters, where it is known to undertake migrations. An active species, the spinner shark pursues prey of pelagic bony fishes that are small enough to swallow whole, such as sardines and small tuna. Its common name is derived from its habit of leaping out of the water and spinning along the length of its body, especially when it is feeding on shoaling fishes. After a gestation period that may exceed 12 months, some 3-15 pups are born near the coast. Young spinner sharks are often caught by shore anglers, although many are misidentified as dusky sharks. They are good to eat. ☐ Spinnerhaai.

Sandbar shark

Carcharhinus plumbeus
av. 150 cm; max. 240 cm

Tooth formula $\dfrac{14 - 1\ or\ 2 - 14}{14 - 1 - 14}$

A stout-bodied, medium-sized shark that can be distinguished from other requiem sharks by its very high, triangular dorsal fin that is placed far forward on the body. The short, rounded snout, presence of a dorsal ridge and pale body without any distinctive marks, further aid identification. Although few are ever seen at the surface, this common coastal shark ranges from the shallow surf zone to depths exceeding 280 m. It prefers offshore banks, especially those opposite rivers such as the Tugela and at Richards Bay, where it feeds on a great variety of small, bottom-dwelling fishes, small sharks, stingrays, and especially octopus. Pregnant females move to special nursery areas where up to 14 pups are born following a 9-12 month gestation. Sandbars periodically provide good angling for shore and boat fishermen, make excellent aquarium specimens, and are a fine source of food, soupfins and leather. □ **Sandbankhaai.**

Blackspot shark

Carcharhinus sealei
av. 60 cm; max. 100 cm

Tooth formula $\dfrac{12 - 2 - 12}{12 - 1 - 12}$

Easily identified by its khaki-grey colour and distinctive black spot on the second dorsal, this attractive small shark is distributed throughout the tropical Indo-Pacific. It is also characterized by the clearly visible chevron-like muscle blocks that lie along each side of the body. Its preference for shallow sandy bays is reflected in its diet of the slow-swimming fishes, squid and prawn species normally found there. Although present throughout the year, most are recorded along Natal's beaches during the summer months, a time that coincides with their mating season. Only two pups are born after

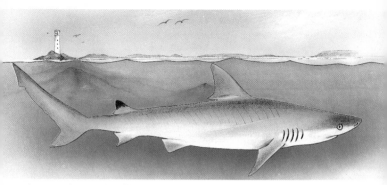

a nine-month gestation. The blackspot shark represents a source of human food in the Far East. Although caught by shore anglers it is not considered a target species. □ **Swartkolhaai.**

Blacktip reef shark

Carcharhinus melanopterus
av. 100 cm; max. 180 cm

Tooth formula $\dfrac{12-1 \text{ or } 2-12}{11-1-11}$

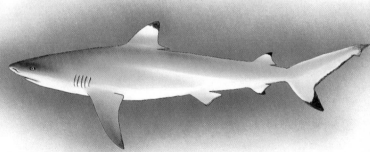

A distinctly tropical shark, closely associated with the coral reef environment and as such found only off Zululand in our waters. Its combination of khaki-coloured body with brilliant black markings on the fin tips, short blunt snout and absence of an interdorsal ridge distinguishes this species from other requiem sharks. The blacktip reef shark ventures into very shallow water, frequently swimming inside coral lagoons and gullies with its fins well exposed. It is a bold species and shows no hesitation in approaching humans swimming underwater or wading. Although too small to cause serious injury, this shark has bitten many people on the leg, and should be treated with respect. Four pups are born in each litter and these probably use coral lagoons as nurseries. The diet consists mostly of small coral reef fishes, octopuses, squid and shrimps. Easily caught on line, this shark makes good eating. □ **Swarttip rifhaai.**

Milkshark

Rhizoprionodon acutus
av. 70 cm; max. 170 cm

Tooth formula $\dfrac{12-1-12}{11-2-11}$

One of the smallest in this family, the milkshark can readily be identified by its slender body, very long depressed snout and a second dorsal that originates well behind the anal fin. This widely distributed warm-water species occurs in coastal waters, ranging from shallow sandy beaches to depths of 200 m, especially near offshore banks. The milkshark is possibly the most abundant shark species off Natal and has become even more numerous since shark nets reduced the numbers of their natural predators. Common throughout the year, most catches are made during summer, coinciding with the mating and pupping seasons. There may be up to eight pups per litter, each pup measuring about 30 cm at birth. Despite its small size, the milkshark's sharp teeth enable it to feed on a wide variety of prey, including many bony fishes, squid, octopuses and shrimps. A frequent and edible catch. □ **Melkhaai.**

Whitetip reef shark (Blunthead shark)

Triaenodon obesus
av. 100 cm; max. 200 cm

This species is easily identified by its stout body and short, broadly rounded snout, the conspicuous white tips to its first dorsal and caudal fins, and also by its relatively large second dorsal fin. Wide-ranging throughout the tropical Indo-Pacific, the whitetip is confined to the coral reef habitat and consequently is found only in shallow water. During daylight it normally rests on the bottom of dark caves, often oblivious of any intrusion by divers. At dusk, however, this territorial shark emerges to patrol its limited home range in pursuit of nocturnal prey such as small coral reef fishes, octopuses, crayfish and crabs. It is a poor swimmer and may remain motionless for hours. Litters of up to five pups have been recorded and it is possible that this species can reach an age of 25 years. Although edible, it has been responsible for cases of ciguatera poisoning. □ **Wittip rifhaai.**

Tiger shark
Galeocerdo cuvieri
av. 250 cm; max. 550 cm

An unmistakable species: not only are the body markings of this huge shark conspicuous, but the short snout, keels on the caudal peduncle, slit-like spiracles and curiously shaped teeth are most distinctive. Distributed throughout the world's temperate and tropical seas, the tiger shark is a relatively common resident along our east coast. This shark appears as content in very shallow water, such as coral lagoons, as it does crossing oceans. Often found in the vicinity of flooding rivers, it is known to scavenge on dead or injured animals: human remains are not infrequently found, emphasizing its potential threat to man. In addition to a great variety of fish and shark species, other dietary items include birds, turtles, dolphins and especially tin cans, plastic bags and other garbage thrown overboard from ships at sea. The tiger shark is the only ovoviviparous species of the requiem shark family and produces large litters (up to 80 pups) during summer. Many tiger sharks are caught on longline and by other means, their flesh being quite edible, skin good for leather and liver rich in vitamin A. □ **Tierhaai.**

Lemon shark

Negaprion acutidens
av. 150 cm; max. 300 cm

This large and robust shark is characterized by its pale brown colour, smooth-edged, pointed teeth and a second dorsal fin that is almost as large as the first. Distributed throughout tropical Indo-Pacific waters, the lemon shark appears confined to shallow bays and reefs, usually swimming sluggishly in gullies near the bottom. This behaviour, together with its colour, often causes it to be mistaken for a ragged-tooth. The lemon shark is quite common along the Zululand coast where it feeds on a wide variety of smaller reef fishes and stingrays. Litters with a maximum of 13 pups are born to the viviparous females during summer. This shark is quite often caught by kite fishermen at St Lucia. Although usually shy of divers, the lemon shark has been known to attack when provoked. ☐ **Geelhaai.**

Blue shark

Prionace glauca
av. 250 cm; max. 400 cm

Clearly a pelagic species with its striking blue colour, slender body, long snout and huge pectoral fins, the blue shark also has a first dorsal fin that is positioned closer to the pelvic than to the pectoral fins. Probably the world's most widely distributed shark, it occurs throughout all oceans from the surface to depths of 150 m and with temperature tolerances from 7 °C to at least 23 °C. Few are ever seen very close to land, and tagging studies

conducted in the United States of America indicate extensive transoceanic migrations. There is great variability in the number of pups born to the viviparous females, with a maximum of 135 recorded. The blue shark is an aggressive predator of small shoaling fishes and squid, and this often results in spectacular lunging attacks at the surface. Birds, lobsters, crabs and marine mammal carrion may also be eaten when available. A common catch of longliners and also a fine angling species that is quite edible and has many other uses. ☐ **Blouhaai.**

HAMMERHEAD SHARKS (SPHYRNIDAE)

Great hammerhead
Sphyrna mokarran
av. 300 cm; max. 600 cm

Their unique head shape makes hammerheads unmistakable. Of the three distinct species that occur in southern African waters, the great hammerhead is not only the largest, it also has an obviously straight edge to the front profile of its 'hammer' and a strikingly high first dorsal fin. This shark is widely distributed throughout the world's warmer coastal waters and may occur from the surface to depths exceeding 80 m. A variety of bony fishes, stingrays and small sharks feature in its diet. Its fairly small mouth limits its ability to attack bathers, although it can be most aggressive to divers and should be treated with caution. The viviparous females produce up to 45 pups. The great hammerhead is often caught by Zululand ski-boaters. ☐ **Groot hamerhaai.**

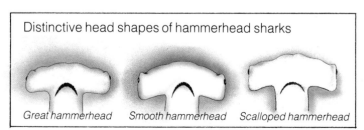

Distinctive head shapes of hammerhead sharks

Great hammerhead *Smooth hammerhead* *Scalloped hammerhead*

Smooth hammerhead
Sphyrna zygaena
av. 180 cm; max. 400 cm

Best identified by the smoothly convex front profile of its 'hammer', which lacks any obvious indentations. A widespread cool-water species, this is the most common hammerhead in Cape waters and usually occurs near the surface, although some range to depths of 20 m. Its inquisitive nature is revealed by its frequent approaches to fishermen in ski-boats, when it often scavenges bait or steals catches. Feeds on a variety of small fish and squid. About 30 pups are born to the viviparous females. The smooth hammerhead makes excellent eating and produces many other by-products. ☐ **Gladde hamerhaai.**

Scalloped hammerhead
Sphyrna lewini
av. 150 cm; max. 400 cm

A distinct indentation in the middle of the otherwise smoothly convex 'hammer' profile distinguishes this species. It is a common warm-water shark of all major oceans and is particularly abundant off Natal where juveniles form large packs during summer. Its diet consists of a variety of small fishes and squid. Litter size may exceed 30 pups and females often show scars as a result of aggressive courtship behaviour. This frequently-caught shark is excellent for food, leather, vitamins and oil. ☐ **Skulprand-hamerhaai.**

SAWFISHES (PRISTIDAE)

Smalltooth sawfish
Pristis pectinata
av. 200 cm; max. 600 cm

In addition to the large saw-like snout, sawfishes also have large pectoral fins that form part of the head and cover the gill openings, while the first dorsal fin is positioned directly over the pelvic fins. There are 28-34 pairs of sharp teeth along the saw, and several rows of pavement-like teeth in the mouth. This widespread subtropical flatfish prefers estuarine or shallow coastal waters, and is common in and around Natal's larger estuaries. The enormous females enter river mouths to drop their 15-20 pups which remain there for their early life. The saw is used for grovelling in the muddy bottom for shellfish or to slash into a shoal of fish to stun the prey. Although not aggressive to man, accidental encounters can prove fatal. The flesh of this sawfish is palatable and is sold fresh on a number of markets throughout the Indo-Pacific. The saw is known to be used for ceremonial purposes by some tribes, and several of the internal organs add power to the concoctions of medicine men. □ **Kleintand-saagvis.**

Largetooth sawfish
Pristis microdon
av. 150 cm; max. 450 cm

Although it resembles the smalltooth sawfish, the largetooth sawfish may be distinguished by its 17-21 pairs of teeth on the saw and by its first dorsal fin which is positioned well in front of the pelvic fins. It is found in the tropical shallows of most oceans, often in the vicinity of river mouths. Diet consists of shellfish and small bony fishes that it swallows whole. Few are caught on line, although some have been caught in shark nets and by offshore trawlermen. Edible. □ **Groottand-saagvis.**

SAWSHARKS (PRISTIOPHORIDAE)

Sixgill sawshark
Pliotrema warreni
av. 90 cm; max. 136 cm

Technically a shark and not a 'flatfish', the sawshark closely resembles a sawfish but is distinguishable by its smaller, more numerous teeth, distinctly separate pectoral fins, and barbels on the saw. There are five species worldwide, only one of which occurs in southern African waters and this one is characterized by having a sixth gill slit. This rather shy, bottom-dwelling fish occurs in shoals on offshore banks at depths of 50 to 150 m, where it feeds on a variety of crabs, prawns, squid and small bony fishes. It is probable that

the saw and its barbels have a sensory function and assist with prey detection. Sawsharks are ovoviviparous and this species gives birth to 5-17 young. To prevent injury to the mother, the teeth of the sawshark embryos lie flat against their saws until after birth. This relatively common species is caught incidentally by bottom trawlers, but seldom marketed despite its edibility. ☐ **Seskief-saaghaai.**

GUITARFISHES (RHINOBATIDAE)

Bowmouth guitarfish (Shortnosed mudskate)
Rhina ancylostoma
av. 150 cm; max. 250 cm

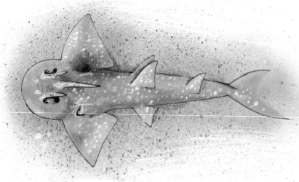

Although resembling an angelshark (page 8), the bowmouth is a true guitarfish, having its curiously undulating mouth situated on the underside and not terminally. Other features include a broadly rounded snout, a first dorsal located just in front of the pelvic fins and distinct rows of horny tubercles along the head and shoulders. This relative of the giant guitarfish is widely distributed throughout the tropical Indo-Pacific, although it is nowhere abundant. Most specimens are netted on the muddy Tugela Bank, while some have been caught elsewhere along the Natal north coast. Very little is known of its life history, although presumably it is ovoviviparous, producing small litters. Diet includes prawns, crabs and other shellfish that are crushed with the pavement-like teeth. Despite being edible it is seldom marketed. ☐ **Boogbek-sandkruiper.**

Giant guitarfish (Giant sandshark)

Rhynchobatus djiddensis
av. 120 cm; max. 300 cm

Guitarfishes are unmistakable with their large pectorals fused to a wedge-shaped forward part of the body. The giant guitarfish is particularly distinctive as a result of its noticeably elongated snout, first dorsal fin situated directly over the pelvic fins, and its deeply forked caudal. This widespread tropical Indo-Pacific guitarfish is very common along Natal's beaches and is generally confined to shallow water (less than 30 m). Large specimens may patrol the outer edges of reefs where they prey on small fish, molluscs and especially crabs and crayfish. Several rows of hard, pavement-like teeth enable them to crush shellfish. This ovoviviparous species produces about four, 60 cm-long pups each summer. The largest of the guitarfish, this is a harmless species that thrives in captivity. In Durban's Seaworld it has shown considerable learning ability and interaction with divers. Although edible, many are released unharmed.
□ **Reuse-sandkruiper.**

Greyspot guitarfish (Greyspot sandshark)

Rhinobatos leucospilus
av. 60 cm; max. 120 cm

This most attractive small guitarfish is best identified by the distinctive grey-blue spots on its pectoral and pelvic fins. It also has a single-lobed dorsal fin and the first dorsal is positioned well back on the body. Endemic to South

Africa's east coast, this species occurs commonly along sandy beaches of
Natal and Transkei. Occasional catches are also made by trawlers operating
to depths of 100 m on the Tugela Bank. This demersal fish is perfectly
camouflaged on the sandy bottom, often covering itself with a fine layer of
sand. Like most guitarfish, it has a small mouth with pavement-like teeth and
feeds on crabs, prawns and molluscs. The ovoviviparous females bear litters
of 2-4 pups, each measuring less than 25 cm. Fine eating.
☐ Gryskol-sandkruiper.

Lesser guitarfish (Lesser sandshark)
Rhinobatos annulatus
av. 80 cm; max. 120 cm

Although often confused with the greyspot guitarfish, the much more
abundant lesser guitarfish can be distinguished by its less obvious, plain
brown body spots. The caudal fin is not forked and the first dorsal is
positioned well behind the pelvic fins. This wide-ranging, tropical Indo-
Pacific species occurs mostly on sandy and muddy bottoms to depths of
50 m. Its diet comprises small shellfish which it crushes with its rows of
strong, pavement-like teeth. Litters of up to four pups are born to the females
each summer and these 60 cm-long young are often found close inshore.
The lesser guitarfish is a particularly common catch by rock and surf anglers
along the entire southern African coast. This fish makes fine eating.
☐ Kleiner sandkruiper.

ELECTRIC RAYS (TORPEDINIDAE)

Marbled electric ray
Torpedo sinuspersici
av. width 50 cm; max. width 90 cm

Electric rays can be distinguished from other flatfishes by the fleshier, almost
circular disc-shaped body and well-developed tail with caudal fin. The
marbled electric ray with its distinctive patterning has two dorsal fins and a
slightly concave shape to its front profile. This widespread Indo-Pacific ray is
common on sandy and muddy bottoms, ranging from the surf zone to depths

exceeding 200 m. It is most cryptic and often hides below a layer of sand with only its eyes and spiracles exposed, presumably in order to surprise unwary prey. The females can bear up to 22 young, each measuring about 10 cm in width. If molested, the ray will emit powerful electric shocks. A common catch by shore anglers and offshore trawlers but, despite its edibility, is seldom if ever marketed.
☐ **Marmer-drilvis.**

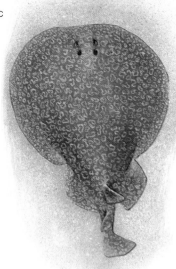

NUMBFISHES (NARKIDAE)

Onefin electric ray
Narke capensis
av. width 25 cm; max. width 35 cm

The single dorsal fin immediately distinguishes this species from the other electric rays found in southern African waters. The near-circular body has a small but distinct indentation in the front, while the noticeably broad pelvic fins are fused on the underside. This endemic species is common on sandy and muddy bottoms, usually at depths of 20 to 150 m. The females are viviparous but little is known of litter size and breeding seasons. Although considerably smaller, this electric ray nevertheless generates a more powerful shock than the marbled electric ray. Most are caught incidentally in trawling operations. It is edible. ☐ **Eenvin-drilvis.**

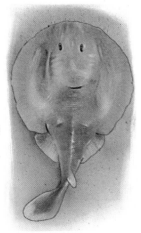

Spearnose skate

Raja alba
av. width 100 cm; max. width 180 cm

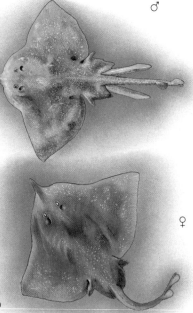

About 23 skate species occur in southern African seas and they can generally be distinguished from rays by having a thicker tail that lacks spines, two small dorsal fins and a pointed snout. The spearnose is identified by its undulating front profile and white body spots. This is a widespread species, especially in the Atlantic Ocean. Although occasional specimens have been caught from the shore, most spearnose occur on offshore banks to depths of 450 m, where they forage on the muddy bottom in search of prey. The diet consists of a variety of organisms, including burrowing molluscs, prawns and small fishes. Females grow larger than males and their oviparous reproduction produces two or more hard egg cases that are attached to suitable underwater objects. Mature males have huge claspers that extend beyond the pelvic fins and may reach the first dorsal. This species, the largest of the skates, is often caught in bottom trawls, but despite its edibility is seldom marketed. □ **Spiesneus-rog.**

Females attach their 'mermaid's purse' egg cases to seaweed or other underwater objects

Bluespotted stingray
Dasyatis kuhlii
av. width 25 cm; max. width 35 cm

This very small stingray with its distinctive bright blue spots differs from the bluespotted ribbontail ray (page 44) by its body shape and more slender tail. Although common throughout the Indo-Pacific, this attractive stingray only periodically visits our shores – mainly during summer. It ventures into very shallow water, usually over sand but in proximity to coral reefs. In spite of its bright colours, the camouflaging ability of this species is considerable. The females are viviparous, although no breeding has been reported from our waters. Food consists mainly of small shrimps and crabs. This stingray is edible.
□ **Bloukol-pylstert.**

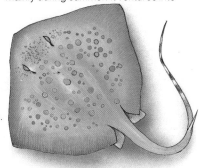

Blue stingray
Dasyatis pastinaca
av. width 50 cm; max. width 75 cm

The golden brown body with blue mottlings is most distinctive. The snout is slightly rounded and the disc is about 1,2 times wider than it is long. The large spiracles (they exceed the eye diameter in size) are noticeable. There is usually only one sharp spine on the tail. This common fish is the most widely distributed stingray in southern African waters and is a popular target for rock and surf anglers. The blue stingray ranges from the shallow, sandy surf zone to depths of 50 m, where it is sometimes netted by prawn trawlers. During spring the females give birth to litters of up to four pups, each measuring about 15 cm across. The blue stingray forages along the bottom in search of prey such as mole crabs, crabs, marine worms and small fishes. Edible, although most are returned alive to the water. □ **Blou pylstert.**

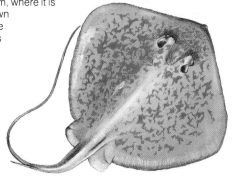

Thorntail stingray
Dasyatis thetidis
av. width 150 cm; max. width 200 cm

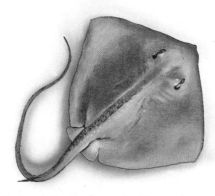

Largest of the stingrays, this wide-ranging Indo-Pacific flatfish may be distinguished by its 'thorny' tail: rows of sharp tubercles that arise along the mid-body and run backwards. Furthermore the disc is about 1,3 times wider than it is long, has a slightly pointed snout and ends in a long tail that has one or two sharply serrated spines. Commonly found in sandy shallows and occasionally within estuaries, the thorntail appears equally at home on offshore banks, sometimes to depths of 400 m. Little is known of its feeding or reproductive behaviour. Only anglers with endless stamina succeed in landing this immensely powerful fish. Edible although seldom marketed.
☐ **Doringstert-pylstert.**

Sharpnose stingray (Brown stingray)
Himantura gerrardi
av. width 50 cm; max. width 90 cm

With its pointed snout and uniform light brown colour, the sharpnose stingray is readily distinguished from most other stingrays. A wide band of closely spaced tubercles runs along the back of the otherwise smooth, disc-shaped body, which is approximately as long as it is wide. The very long, whip-like tail may reach a length 2½ times that of the disc width. This widespread Indo-Pacific species is abundant off sandy shores and in muddy estuaries along much of our east coast. Some have been trawled to depths of 50 m. Litters of at least two pups are born during summer and the young often enter estuaries to mature. The sharpnose stingray is exclusively a bottom-dwelling species and feeds on prawns, crabs and small crayfish. Its flesh makes fine eating. ☐ **Skerpneus-pylstert.**

Honeycomb stingray (Marble or Leopard stingray)
Himantura uarnak
av. width 60 cm; max. width 200 cm

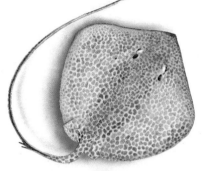

This strikingly patterned stingray is unmistakable, although it closely corresponds to the sharpnose stingray in shape and body proportions. The young are born with leopard-like markings but, with age, these gradually change to a marbled pattern. Widespread throughout the tropical Indo-Pacific, the honeycomb stingray is common along beaches of our east coast. Litters of up to five pups are born during summer and many of these young enter estuaries during their early life. Small crabs and prawns constitute its diet, much of which may be foraged in very shallow water. Anglers are often lacerated by the couple of sharp, poisonous spines found at the base of the very long tail. This large and powerful ray is a popular target for heavy-tackle anglers; though edible, most are returned unharmed. □ **Heuningkoek-pylstert.**

Butterfly ray (Diamond ray, Backwater)
Gymnura natalensis
av. width 120 cm;
max. width 250 cm

There can be no mistaking this species as it has a body that is distinctly wider than it is long. Its short tail is armed with one or two stout, sharp spines while the tip of its snout bears a small projection. This endemic stingray favours turbid water and is often found in estuaries or trawled offshore to depths of 70 m. Although primarily bottom-living, the butterfly ray is an active species and may congregate into midwater shoals. Swimming close to the bottom facilitates preying on the small fishes, soles and crabs that constitute its diet. Gravid females are commonly seen during summer and produce up to ten pups per litter. As one of the strongest stingrays, this species is a popular catch during angling tournaments; most are released unharmed. □ **Vlinderrog.**

Bluespotted ribbontail ray
Taeniura lymma
av. width 30 cm; max. width 75 cm (?)

In addition to its strikingly bold colour pattern, this stingray may be characterized by its oval-shaped body and thick tail that approximates body length. Although uncommon in South Africa, its abundance increases sharply from Zululand northwards. The bluespotted ribbontail prefers tropical lagoons or sandy shallows close to reefs, often covering itself with a layer of sand to aid camouflage. Its diet includes shrimps, worms and hermit crabs, although most of its life history remains unknown. Seldom caught by anglers but certainly a popular sighting for skindivers.
□ **Blougekolde lintstertrog.**

Round ribbontail ray (Fantail)
Taeniura melanospilos
av. width 130 cm; max. width 200 cm

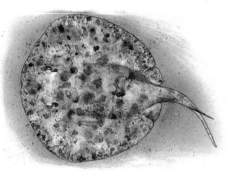

This enormous ray can best be identified by its circular body shape and distinctly mottled colours. The small eyes are slightly elevated above the body and each is protected by a horny projection. There are several short bands of tubercles on the otherwise smooth body and the stout tail carries one or two spines. Widely distributed through the Indian Ocean, the round ribbontail is common along the Natal coast where it ranges from the surf zone to depths of 500 m, and is often found in the vicinity of river mouths. As it is one of the heaviest stingrays to be caught, this ribbontail is popular with heavy-tackle anglers. □ **Ronde lintstertrog.**

Duckbill

Pteromylaeus bovinus
av. width 100 cm; max. width 175 cm

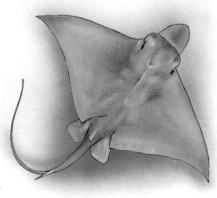

With its pronounced head and long, fleshy snout, diamond-shaped body and the small dorsal fin positioned between the pelvic fins, the duckbill is easily identified. Although this midwater species is of Atlantic origin, most local records are from Natal's sandy beaches or larger estuaries. This is an active species, occasionally grouping into small shoals, and leaping from the water in an apparent attempt to shed parasites. The very powerful rows of pavement teeth permit it to feed on hard shells, crabs and a variety of small fishes. The females give birth to live young, usually four per litter. Popular as a tournament fish, but most are returned to the water unharmed. □ **Arendrog.**

Bullray

Myliobatus aquila
av. width 55 cm; max. width 150 cm

Although similar to the duckbill, the bullray is readily distinguished by its shorter snout and by having its dorsal fin positioned behind the pelvic fins. Also of Atlantic origin, this species predominates along Cape shores and is only occasionally reported from Natal and Transkei. This coastal species frequents sandy shores and often enters estuaries. At times the bullray appears gregarious and small groups may be seen near the surface, sometimes leaping into the air. The diet consists mainly of sand mussels and mole crabs that are crushed with the massive teeth. Litters of 3-7 pups are born in shallow water. This strong fish makes a fine target for sport anglers. □ **Bulrog.**

Spotted eagleray (Bonnetray)
Aetobatus narinari
av. width 130 cm; max. width 200 cm

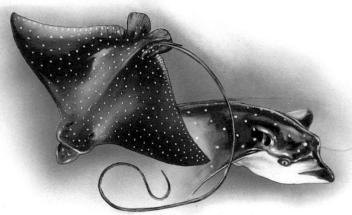

Among the most beautiful of rays, this midwater eagleray can be instantly recognized by its diamond-shaped body and distinctive coloration. The prominent head with its fleshy, projecting snout is also noticeable. The whip-like tail is exceptionally long and usually armed with two sharp spines. Found throughout the world's warmer surface waters, this species is most common along much of our east coast during summer. It forages around rocky shores, jetties and piers, where it feeds on mussels and oysters which it crushes easily with its powerful bands of pavement-like teeth. The viviparous females produce litters of up to four pups after a one-year gestation. Although occasionally caught by anglers, the spotted eagleray is more popular with skindivers who can witness its graceful, bird-like movement through the water.

□ Spikkel-arendrog.

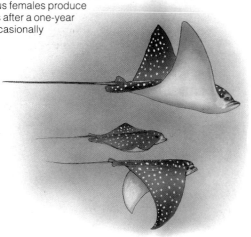

Devilray
Mobula diabolus
av. width 100 cm; max. width 180 cm

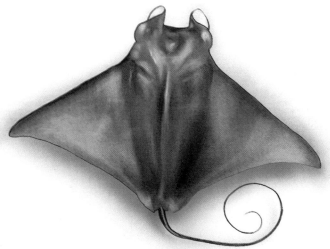

Although similar in many respects to the eaglerays, mantas may be distinguished by their cephalic fins, projections that point forward from the head. The devilray has its wide mouth located on the underside of the head. This species prefers tropical surface waters and is confined to the Indo-Pacific region, often near the edges of coral reefs. The wide mouth and large gill slits enable it to filter planktonic food from huge quantities of seawater by means of a fine network of gill filaments. The devilray is the smallest of the mantas and attains maturity at less than 100 cm disc width. The ovoviviparous female nourishes the two embryos with uterine milk prior to their hatching at a size of about 30 cm disc width. It is the most common manta and its harmless, inquisitive nature often delights divers. It is not caught by anglers, but quite a few become entangled in shark nets.
□ Duiwelrog.

Manta ray
Manta birostris
av. width 350 cm; max. width 700 cm

This enormous ray with its distinctive shape, cephalic fins and mouth located terminally, is not easily misidentified. Its range includes the warm temperate waters of all oceans, and it invariably lives close to the surface. Although less common than *M. diabolus*, the manta ray is regularly reported, especially when it leaps clear of the water, falling back with a splash that can be heard for some distance. This filter-feeding ray consumes large quantities of plankton: underwater observations clearly show its huge open mouth when feeding, sometimes assisted by the cephalic fins to direct larger prey into the mouth. It is known that two young are born to the ovoviviparous females, although little else has been reported about this species' reproduction. This ray has often been described as dangerous, but it is in fact quite harmless, despite its size and weight (nearly two tonnes). Few specimens are ever caught other than those trapped in shark nets. ☐ **Manta.**

Ancestry of sharks and rays

The first sharks are thought to have appeared some 400 million years ago, at a time when fishes in general were evolving to become a major form of life in the oceans. Although mostly smaller than the sharks we know today, those ancestral fishes were not unlike our modern sharks in appearance and anatomy. Their abundance increased at such a rate that by 300 million years ago, they dominated life in the oceans and progressively evolved more advanced swimming, feeding and reproductive techniques. This continued until some 100 million years ago, when most modern groups of sharks came into existence. Since then their evolution has followed two broad patterns, one being the main shark line that today embraces some 350 species. The other direction has been towards a bottom-dwelling existence, resulting in the evolution of flat-bodied fishes such as skates and stingrays, which now number some 430 species worldwide. The separation of these two groups is not entirely distinct and many transitional forms exist – such as the guitarfishes, angelsharks, sawfishes and others. Flat-bodied cartilaginous fishes are, therefore, seen to be the more recent members evolved in this order, with the true sharks having undergone rather little change since Devonian times, some 400 million years ago.

Schematic representation of evolution in cartilaginous fishes

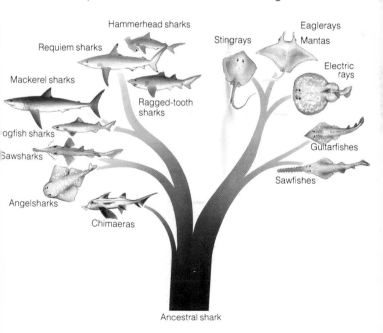

Hammerhead sharks

Requiem sharks

Mackerel sharks

Ragged-tooth sharks

ogfish sharks

Sawsharks

Angelsharks

Chimaeras

Eaglerays

Stingrays

Mantas

Electric rays

Guitarfishes

Sawfishes

Ancestral shark

Anatomy

Although the fishes described in this book are immensely varied in shape and size, they all share one common feature: their skeletons are composed entirely of cartilage and not hard bone, as in the case of bony fishes. A further feature unique to this class of fishes is the numerous gill openings (usually six or seven); bony fishes have only a single opening. Their fins, too, are distinctive, being composed of fibrous supporting filaments and not rays or spines as in other fishes. Certainly some sharks and rays do have spines associated with their fins, but these are more of a defensive nature than a structural necessity. Whereas most bony fishes are covered with scales, many cartilaginous fishes have an outer layer of skin composed of sharp, toothlike projections known as dermal denticles. This feature gives sharks their characteristic sandpaper-like texture. These denticles are in fact minute teeth and, where they occur in the jaws, are enlarged to form the several rows of dentition. The actual shape and size of teeth varies greatly and may range from flat, pavement types to razor-sharp cutting teeth.

There are several other features unique to cartilaginous fishes, such as the spiracle, a rudimentary gill slit that can provide additional oxygenated water to the gills in slow-moving or bottom-living species; the claspers in male fish, being paired organs used for internal fertilization; and the spiral valve, a section of the intestine that is internally coiled so as to increase the absorptive surface area.

The diversity of shape in cartilaginous fishes is considerable and ranges from typical shark-like forms to the flattened body shape of batoid fishes such as rays and sandsharks.

Typical shark

Sharks usually have fusiform bodies, almost round in cross-section and mostly with well-developed fins to facilitate swimming.

Anatomy of a shark

1 nostril; 2 eye; 3 brain; 4 spiracle;
5 nerve cord; 6 vertebrae;
7 muscles; 8 testis; 9 first dorsal fin;
10 dorsal spine;
11 second dorsal fin;
12 caudal fin; 13 muscles;

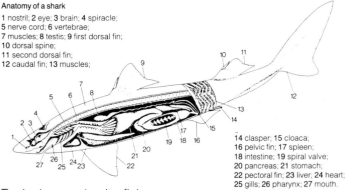

14 clasper; 15 cloaca;
16 pelvic fin; 17 spleen;
18 intestine; 19 spiral valve;
20 pancreas; 21 stomach;
22 pectoral fin; 23 liver; 24 heart;
25 gills; 26 pharynx; 27 mouth.

Typical ray and guitarfish

Obvious external differences prevent confusion between rays and sharks. Of these, the positioning of the gill openings and the arrangement of the pectoral fins are most characteristic. Rays have their gill openings situated on the underside of the head as opposed to the lateral gill slits of sharks, and their pectoral fins are enlarged into the typical flattened disc. In true sharks the pectoral fins never extend forward of the gill openings. Guitarfishes are more shark-like in general shape, but they too have gill slits opening on the underside and much enlarged pectoral fins which give them their distinctive shovel-shaped heads.

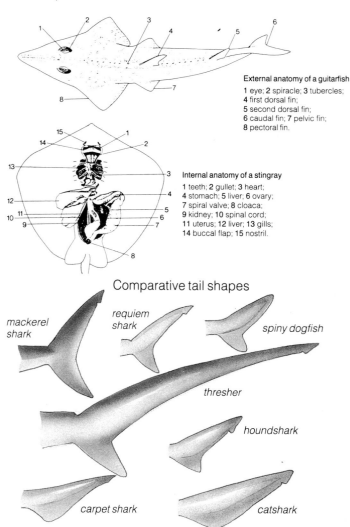

External anatomy of a guitarfish

1 eye; 2 spiracle; 3 tubercles;
4 first dorsal fin;
5 second dorsal fin;
6 caudal fin; 7 pelvic fin;
8 pectoral fin.

Internal anatomy of a stingray

1 teeth; 2 gullet; 3 heart;
4 stomach; 5 liver; 6 ovary;
7 spiral valve; 8 cloaca;
9 kidney; 10 spinal cord;
11 uterus; 12 liver; 13 gills;
14 buccal flap; 15 nostril.

Comparative tail shapes

mackerel shark

requiem shark

spiny dogfish

thresher

houndshark

carpet shark

catshark

The senses of sharks

Cartilaginous fishes generally have well-developed and sometimes specialized senses that aid survival in the harsh marine environment. Obviously individual species have variously developed senses, depending on their habitat and behaviour. The eye is similar in structure to that of most vertebrates, although it has a particularly well-developed tapetum lucidum, the reflective layer that enhances low-light vision. Many shark species have excellent vision, especially those pelagic predators that hunt in clear water. Some sharks have a transparent third eyelid, known as the nictitating membrane, that protects the eye during attack.

The nostrils of sharks and rays are not used for respiration, but operate exclusively as olfactory organs. In some species their function is enhanced by nasal barbels that also fulfil a sensory purpose. The ability of sharks to detect prey may often be due to their good sense of smell: some apparently are able to trace blood in concentrations as low as one part per million.

Ampullae of Lorenzini are small vesicles that occur on the head of most sharks and enable them to sense weak electrical fields. This allows sharks to track hidden prey, such as fish that may be lying below layers of sand. By gently pressing the snout of a freshly killed shark, the jelly-like substance of the ampullae can be seen.

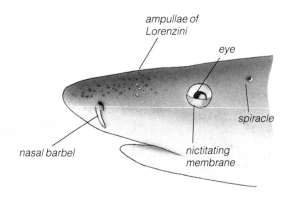

Teeth

Whereas most vertebrate animals, including bony fishes, have teeth set in sockets in the jaws, cartilaginous fishes are unique in having several rows of teeth that are continuously replaced. These teeth are derived from the skin and are enlargements of the dermal denticles that cover the body of most sharks.

Each tooth has a root, base and crown, the latter consisting of a central cusp often flanked by lateral cusplets. As the teeth are variously used for seizing, cutting or crushing prey, so the shape varies and is usually indicative of the species' feeding behaviour. The teeth may also be of value in the identification of species. (For explanation of tooth formulas, see page 3.)

Typical crushing teeth

houndshark (p. 21)

sharpnose stingray (p. 42)

guitarfish (pp. 36-38)

Typical seizing teeth

spotted gullyshark (p. 22)

banded catshark (p. 18)

ragged-tooth shark (p. 12)

Typical cutting teeth

upper
lower
great white shark (p. 13)

Zambezi shark (p. 26)

tiger shark (p. 31)

copper shark (p. 24)

blackspot shark (p. 28)

soupfin (p. 20)

milkshark (p. 30)

blacktip shark (p. 25)

Feeding

An outstanding feature of the cartilaginous fishes is their exclusively carnivorous diet: no herbivores exist in this group. Nevertheless there is a wide diversity of feeding strategies that range from indiscriminate filter-

feeding to selection and pursual of specific prey. Notably, the larger species, such as the basking shark, whale shark and manta ray are filter feeders, straining their planktonic food from the massive volume of water that passes over the filtering mechanism of the gills.

Whale shark filter-feeding

A large proportion of sharks and rays live on or close to the bottom and many feed on shellfish and other burrowing animals that have to be routed out of the substrate. Whereas sawfish may use their saws for this purpose, large rays flap and 'blow' at one spot to create a depression in the sand from which food is captured. Significantly, many of these fishes have large spiracles situated on top of their bodies, so that clean water can be taken into the gill chamber without mud from below clogging the respiratory system. Invariably the bottom-living sharks and rays have pavement-like teeth suitable for crushing their hard-shelled prey.

Sawfish uses its saw to forage in sand for food and to slash at its prey

Ray 'blowing' and flapping to expose food buried in sand

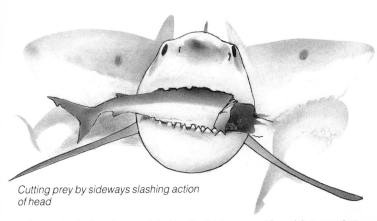

Cutting prey by sideways slashing action of head

Some sharks have long, pointed teeth which are used for seizing prey that is then swallowed whole. In contrast, many others have triangular teeth with razor-sharp, serrated edges so that when the shark uses a sideways action of its head, it can cut its prey into sections. These sharks can therefore tackle prey that is larger than a single mouthful.

There are numerous other adaptations and strategies for feeding and you may find it interesting to study the shark's anatomy in order to gain some insight into its feeding habits.

Jaw action of requiem shark

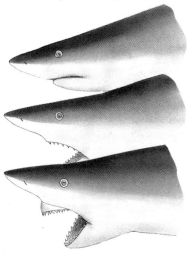

The teeth of many pelagic sharks are not always obvious as the lower jaw can fit snugly into the upper, providing an almost unbroken profile to the streamlined head. However, when the mouth is opened wide, the movable upper jaw appears to 'dislocate' and is thrust forward, the teeth being well presented in the process. This ability is put to good effect when attacking prey, but sharks often flex their jaws when not feeding. Such 'yawning' is not clearly understood.

Reproduction

Advanced and diverse methods of reproduction have evolved within the group of cartilaginous fishes. In contrast to bony fishes which usually shed vast quantities of eggs and sperm into the water where fertilization occurs, sharks and rays are internally fertilized and produce only a small number of young. Whereas the newly hatched young of bony fishes are underdeveloped and highly vulnerable to their environment, cartilaginous fishes produce offspring that are much better developed at the time of birth. The long gestation period and large yolk supply ensure that the embryos are exceptionally well protected and nourished and hence pups are large and well-developed when they are born, enhancing their chances of survival.

Male sharks possess a pair of claspers that inseminate the female, although the actual process of mating has seldom been observed. Development after fertilization can broadly be divided into three groups.

The advanced modes of reproduction have probably contributed to the evolutionary success of sharks in producing well-developed offspring that are subject to a low natural mortality. However, the small number of pups produced does make sharks and rays more vulnerable to a high fishing mortality, and this is certain to be the main reason why many of the shark fisheries have collapsed.

Typical life cycles

Oviparous fish

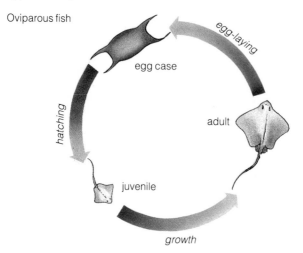

Oviparous development is the most primitive form of reproduction. Here the embryo with its adequate yolk supply is encased in a 'mermaid's purse', laid by the female and attached to a suitable underwater object, after which development continues before hatching. Examples are the spearnose skate and catsharks.

Ovoviviparous fish

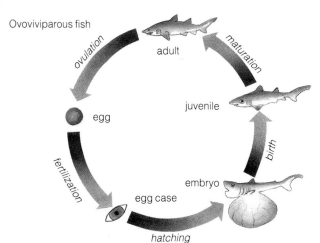

Ovoviviparous development is the most common among sharks and involves the hatching of the embryo while it is still in the mother's uterus. Here development continues and the embryo is nourished by its own yolk sac, before being born in an advanced state. Examples of this include the dogfish sharks, guitarfishes and most stingrays. An added feature of ovoviviparity is that in some species the embryos swallow other yolk sacs in order to obtain nourishment. This is referred to as oviphagy or uterine cannibalism, and the ragged-tooth shark is the best known example.

Viviparous fish

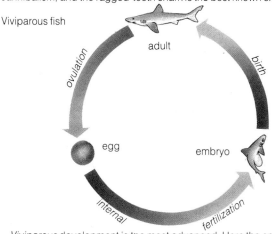

Viviparous development is the most advanced. Here the embryo not only develops within the uterus, it is also nourished by it, either through a placental connection or by a form of uterine milk that bathes the embryos. Examples are the requiem sharks and hammerheads.

Shark attack

The subject of shark attack engenders fear and emotion in many people. Much of this is based on misleading information because, in truth, the problem of shark attack is highly overrated. The majority of shark species are completely harmless, and most do not exceed a maximum length of 2 m. Among the larger sharks, only 27 species (20%) worldwide have ever been implicated in any form of attack and only four, namely the great white, tiger, Zambezi and oceanic whitetip sharks, are potentially dangerous.

Obviously these species should be treated with respect and care, but it is incorrect to term them 'man-eating'. Humans do not form part of any shark's diet and the occasional attack is probably the result of 'investigation' or mistaken identity for seals and other marine mammals. Recent research has shown that many of the attacks are likely to be of an aggressive or defensive nature. This would explain why victims usually have far less serious wounds than would be the case if the shark were actively feeding.

Documentation of shark attacks reveals that some 30-50 cases are reported worldwide each year, with only one or two cases in southern Africa. Very few of these attacks are fatal and pro rata certainly do not compare with the number of motor car accidents, or dog attacks for that matter. Humans are far more dangerous to sharks than *vice versa* – and many species of shark are endangered by man's exploitation. Just as one would not advocate eliminating all motor cars and dogs, so too should sharks be spared from needless killing.

Prevention

Man has devised many schemes to protect him from possible shark attack. The most widely used preventive measure, and undoubtedly the most successful, is that of gill nets, such as those found off Natal's beaches. While not presenting an impenetrable barrier to sharks, these nets are most efficient in trapping sharks, thereby reducing their abundance in a particular region. Obviously one can neither hope nor desire to eliminate all sharks, and as a result numerous other schemes have been under study. These include various chemicals and dyes, bubble barriers and electrical fields. The latter has been developed to an advanced stage in South Africa and relies on electrical pulses influencing the shark's nervous system.

Despite the vast sums of money spent on anti-shark measures, none is as effective as the personal precautions one should adopt. Analysis of previous shark attacks reveals a distinct pattern which indicates that attacks are more likely:

- in muddy or turbid areas near river mouths
- when there is blood or animal waste in the water
- at night, dawn and dusk
- where there are concentrations of fish (for example, sardines)
- along outer edges of reefs and channels
- when swimming alone

By being aware of the above and taking the relevant precautions, the possibility of ever being attacked by a shark is minimal.

Uses of sharks

More useful products can be derived from sharks than from any other group of fishes and practically every part of the body can be utilized. The most important is obviously food, because virtually all shark species are edible. As in bony fishes, the quality of the flesh varies, with dogfish sharks, makos and soupfin sharks commanding the best prices.

In order to make shark flesh palatable, it is necessary to remove the odour produced by the urea and ammonia that is found in the tissues. This is easily achieved by rapidly bleeding and cleaning the shark after capture and subsequently soaking the fillets in saltwater before cooking them. Shark meat is also used to make a type of biltong, and in the production of fishmeal for livestock.

In Eastern countries shark fins are in great demand for making a speciality soup. After drying, the fibrous fin rays are boiled to provide a clear and delicious extract. The liver of the sharks is equally valued for its special oils and vitamin A content. The oils may be used in lamps, vitamin supplements and the production of squalene, a highly polyunsaturated fat.

The skin of sharks has several uses. It not only makes fine sandpaper known as shagreen, but during the last century was used to cover the handles of German soldiers' swords. Once the rough denticles are removed with acid, the skin of many species – especially the catsharks – makes excellent leather. The jaws of sharks are valued for ornamental or ceremonial objects, while the backbones can be made into walking sticks. Sharks also represent an important source of biological specimens and most natural history students dissect the spiny dogshark during their practical training.

Perhaps one of the best uses of sharks lies in their strength and angling potential. Many battles have been fought and lost between huge sharks and anglers, and sharks remain popular as sport fish.

Clearly then, sharks do not deserve their bad reputation. Their value to man is immense and, considering their role in the ecosystem, sharks should be carefully managed for future generations.

The basking shark is vulnerable to being harpooned when it shoals for courtship and feeding.

Glossary

abdomen: belly.

anal: region of the vent, or anal fin.

anterior: front or head region.

axil: the inner region of the fin base in paired fins, roughly corresponding to the human armpit.

barbel: a fleshy projection near the mouth, often used for taste or touch.

batoid: a flat cartilaginous fish, i.e. skate or ray.

benthic: bottom-living.

bony fishes or teleosts: fishes with a true bone skeleton.

cartilage: gristle, firm elastic tissue that forms all or part of a vertebrate skeleton.

cartilaginous: (1) composed of gristle; (2) descriptive of fishes such as sharks, skates and rays, which lack a true bone skeleton.

caudal fin: the unpaired fin at the tail of most fishes.

caudal peduncle: the narrow region that attaches the caudal fin to the body.

caudal notch: an indentation at the base of the caudal fin in sharks.

cephalic: the region of the head.

ciguatera: a fish toxin, dangerous to man, but found only in isolated tropical localities.

circumtropical: throughout tropical regions.

claspers: rod-like, grooved processes attached to the pelvic fins of male sharks, skates, rays and guitarfishes. Used to transmit sperm during copulation.

continental shelf: the shallow ledge forming the seabed that surrounds land masses, usually taken to the arbitrary depth of 200 m.

cusp: a point, e.g. as in teeth.

demersal: living close to the seabed.

denticles: tooth-like projections such as the scales which completely cover the bodies of cartilaginous fishes.

dentition: the characteristic arrangement of teeth.

dermal denticles: tough, often tooth-like projections of the skin.

disc: the fused head and fin region of some depressed fish, e.g. skates and rays.

disc width: the 'wingspan' of rays.

dorsal: pertaining to the upper or back region.

dorsal ridge: a fold of tough skin that runs along the upper body of some sharks.

embryo: a developing organism prior to hatching or birth.

fins: any of the firm appendages that are the organs of propulsion and balance in fishes and some other aquatic animals. Most fishes have paired fins (pelvic and pectoral) and unpaired fins (dorsal, anal and caudal), the former corresponding to the limbs of higher vertebrates.

genus: a group of closely related animal or plant species.

gill: the respiratory organ of fishes and other aquatic animals.

gill opening: variable number of openings behind the head, through which exhaled water is passed.

gravid: pregnant.

height (in fins, usually the dorsals): the vertical distance from the tip of the fin to the body.

Indo-Pacific: embracing the Indian and usually the western Pacific oceans.

invertebrate: an animal without a backbone.

keel: a flat, longitudinal ridge that occurs on either side of the caudal peduncle in some gamefishes and sharks.

lateral: on the side.

lateral line: a series of sensory tubercles forming a raised line along either side of the body of some fishes.

litter: the newly born young of a shark, skate or ray.

longline: a continuous line or cord, sometimes 50 km long, with interspaced baited hooks and floats, set by commercial fishermen for the capture of large fish.

mermaid's purse: a popular name given to the egg cases of oviparous species.

mollusc: an invertebrate animal, usually with an outer shell, e.g. mussels, perlemoen, cuttlefish.

oviparous: producing young by laying egg cases in which the embryos continue to develop after the egg cases are shed.

ovoviviparous: producing young from egg cases in which the embryos develop within the maternal body, and are expelled at hatching.

pavement teeth: the 'cobbled' arrangement of teeth in a number of cartilaginous fishes.

peduncle: *see* caudal peduncle.

pelagic: living in the open sea, especially near the surface.

pelvic: the region, posterior to the belly, to which paired pelvic fins are attached.

plankton: small animal or plant organisms suspended in the water column.

pup: a newly born shark, skate or ray.

rostrum: a projecting snout or beak.

scuba: acronym for 'Self Contained Underwater Breathing Apparatus', i.e. aqualungs.

sensory: capable of perceiving external stimuli.

serrate: sharp, almost saw-like, e.g. some spines.

spiracles: respiratory openings behind the eyes in some sharks and rays.

temperate: of mild temperature. In geography, usually the regions between the Tropic of Cancer and the Arctic Circle and the Tropic of Capricorn and the Antarctic Circle. In fishes this infers that their distribution is principally confined to these regions.

terminal: towards the end.

tooth formula: the typical and regular arrangement of teeth, especially those of sharks.

total length: the length of a fish measured from the tip of the snout to the tip of the tail. Where the caudal fin is forked, total length is measured from the tip of the snout to the tip of the longer lobe folded down.

ventral: pertaining to the lower region or underside of a fish.

viviparous: bearing live young after the development of an embryo or embryos within the maternal body.

yolk-sac: a sac containing the remains of the egg-yolk, often temporarily suspended from the underside of the newly hatched fish.

Further reading

Many books and scientific references were consulted in the compilation of this pocket guide. Not all are listed here, but those of major importance and of possible interest for further reading are given.

*Bass, A.J., D'Aubrey, J.D. and Kistnasamy, N. 1973. Sharks of the east coast of southern Africa. I. The genus *Carcharhinus* (Carcharhinidae). *Invest. Rep. oceanogr. Res. Inst.*, (33): 1-168.
*Bass, A.J., D'Aubrey, J.D. and Kistnasamy, N. 1975a. Sharks of the east coast of southern Africa. II. The families Scyliorhinidae and Pseudotriakidae. *Invest. Rep. oceanogr. Res. Inst.*, (37): 1-63.
*Bass, A.J., D'Aubrey, J.D. and Kistnasamy, N. 1975b. Sharks of the east coast of southern Africa. III. The families Carcharhinidae (excluding *Mustelus* and *Carcharhinus*) and Sphyrnidae. *Invest. Rep. oceanogr. Res. Inst.*, (38): 1-100.
*Bass, A.J., D'Aubrey, J.D. and Kistnasamy, N. 1975c. Sharks of the east coast of southern Africa. IV. The families Odontaspididae, Scapanorhynchidae, Isuridae, Cetorhinidae, Alopiidae, Orectolobidae and Rhiniodontidae. *Invest. Rep. oceanogr. Res. Inst.*, (39): 1-102.
*Bass, A.J., D'Aubrey, J.D. and Kistnasamy, N. 1975d. Sharks of the east coast of southern Africa. V. The families Hexanchidae, Chlamydoselachidae, Heterodontidae, Pristiophoridae and Sqatinidae. *Invest. Rep. oceanogr. Res. Inst.*, (43): 1-50.
*Bass, A.J., D'Aubrey, J.D. and Kistnasamy, N. 1976. Sharks of the east coast of southern Africa. VI. The families Oxynotidae, Squalidae, Dalatiidae and Echinorhinidae. *Invest. Rep. oceanogr. Res. Inst.*, (45): 1-103.
Castro, J.I. 1983. *The sharks of north American waters*. College Station, Texas, A and M University Press: 1-180.
Compagno, J.V. 1984. FAO species catalogue. Sharks of the world: An annotated and illustrated catalogue of shark species known to date. FAO Fisheries Synopsis (125) Vol. 4, pts. 1 and 2.
Davies, D.H. 1964. *About Sharks and Shark Attack*. Shuter and Shooter, Pietermaritzburg.
Garrick, J.A.F. 1982. Sharks of the genus *Carcharhinus*. NOAA technical report, NMFS Circular (445) 1982: 1-194.
Hodgson, E.S. and Mathewson, R.F. (eds). 1978. *Sensory Biology of Sharks, Skates and Rays*. Office of Naval Research, Arlington.
Smith, M.M. and Heemstra, P.C. (eds). 1986. *Smith's Sea Fishes*. Macmillan, Johannesburg.
Van der Elst, R. 1981. *A Guide to the Common Sea Fishes of southern Africa*. Struik, Cape Town.
Wallace, J.H. 1967. The batoid fishes of the east coast of southern Africa, 1: Sawfishes and guitarfishes. *Invest. Rep. oceanogr. Res. Inst.*, (15): 1-32.
*Wallace, J.H. 1967. The batoid fishes of the east coast of southern Africa, 2: Manta, eagle, duckbill, cownose, butterfly and sting rays. *Invest. Rep. oceanogr. Res. Inst.*, (16): 1-56.
*Wallace, J.H. 1967. The batoid fishes of the east coast of southern Africa, 3: Skates and electric rays. *Invest. Rep. oceanogr. Res. Inst.*, (17): 1-62.

Wallett, T. 1978. *Shark attack in Southern African Waters and treatment of victims*. Struik, Cape Town.

* Limited numbers of these reports can be purchased at nominal cost from the Librarian, Oceanographic Research Institute, P O Box 10712, Marine Parade 4056.

INDEX